spot the Difference

Published and distributed by
TOBAR LIMITED
The Old Aerodrome, Worlingham, Beccles,
Suffolk, NR34 7SP, UK

www.tobar.co.uk

This edition printed 2008

© 2008 Arcturus Publishing Limited

Puzzles Copyright © 2008 Puzzle Press Ltd

Printed in Singapore

ISBN: 978-1-903230-32-9

spot the Difference

100 AMAZING PHOTOGRAPHIC PUZZLES

SPOT THE DIFFERENCE

Attention to detail is often said to be lacking in the modern, bustling world in which we live.

Have you an eye for detail? Just how good will you prove to be at spotting when something is different? These pictures will test your powers of observation to the limit.

The puzzles range through five levels of observation, from Warm-Up to Expert, with the numbers of eyes indicating the difficulty levels: we reckon you'll need more than one pair for some of these intricate photos!

If you enjoy the stimulus of working against the clock, then we can give you target times:

⏳ Puzzles in the Warm-Up section should take no more than five minutes to solve

⏳ Standard puzzles should take anywhere between six to eight minutes

⏳ Challenging puzzles between seven and nine minutes

⏳ Tough puzzles about ten minutes

⏳ Expert puzzles may take ten to fifteen minutes each

If you can solve any of these puzzles in less time than recommended, then you really are observant.

In addition, there are puzzles which challenge you to spot just one difference, or to spot where things are hidden or missing; there are also reflected pictures, 'spot the same', negatives, and many other picture puzzles to provide variety, and to add to your puzzling pleasure.

Tick off the changes as you find them, then check to see if you are right, by turning to the solutions at the back of the book.

CONTENTS

EXAMPLE

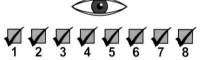

1 2 3 4 5 6 7 8

PUZZLES

HOT AIR BALLOONS

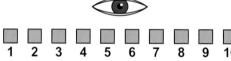

| 1 | 2 | 3 | 4 | 5 | 6 | 7 | 8 | 9 | 10 |

SPOT THE DOLL

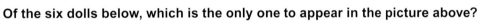

Of the six dolls below, which is the only one to appear in the picture above?

ONE DIFFERENCE EACH

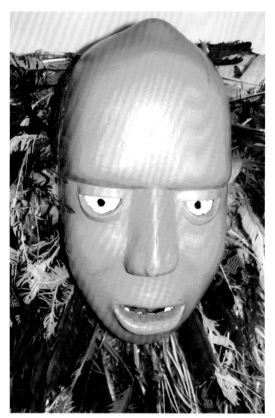

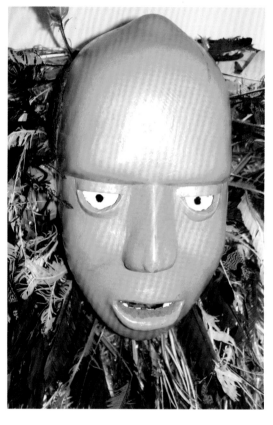

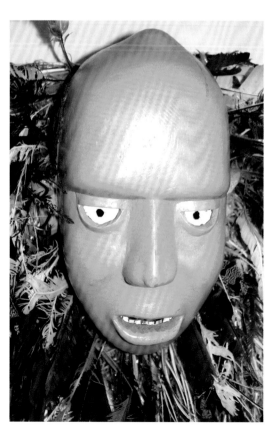

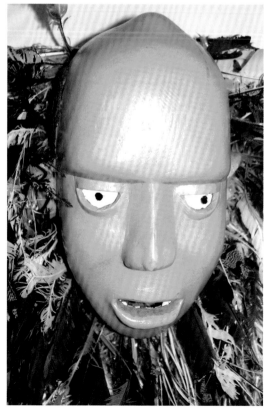

GIRL WITH TOYS

4

| 1 | 2 | 3 | 4 | 5 | 6 | 7 | 8 |

1

2

3

4

5

SCHOOLKIDS

1 2 3 4 5 6 7 8 9

TEMPUS FUGIT

EASTER EGGS

1

2

3

4

5

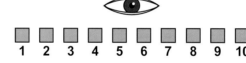

| 1 | 2 | 3 | 4 | 5 | 6 | 7 | 8 | 9 | 10 |

CHRISTMAS DECORATIONS

1

2

3

1 2 3 4 5 6 7 8 9 10 11 12

4

5

THE BOURSE

1

2

3

4

5

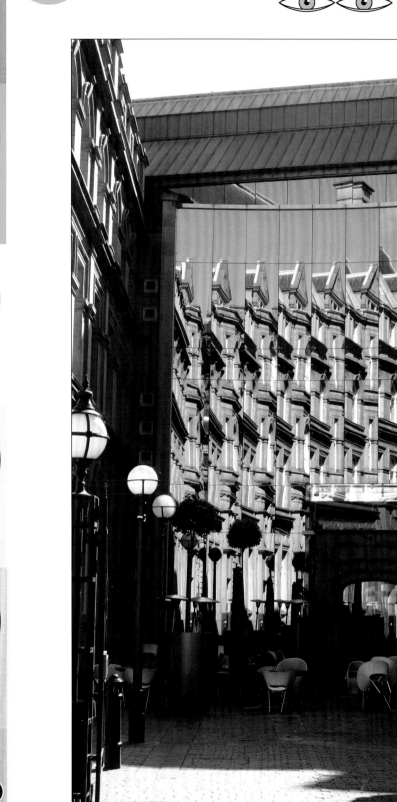

THE BOURSE

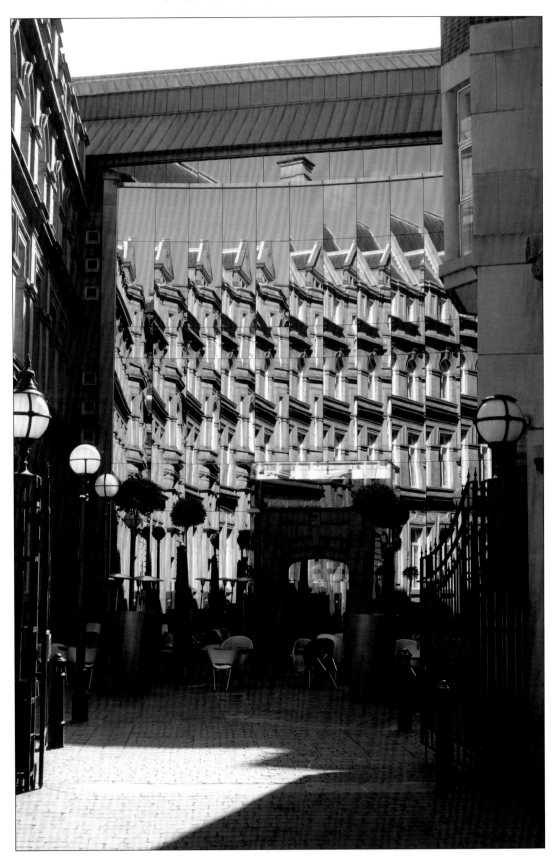

1

2

3

4

5

CHEERS!

1

2

3

1	2	3	4	5	6	7	8	9	10

4

5

MATCH THE NEGATIVE

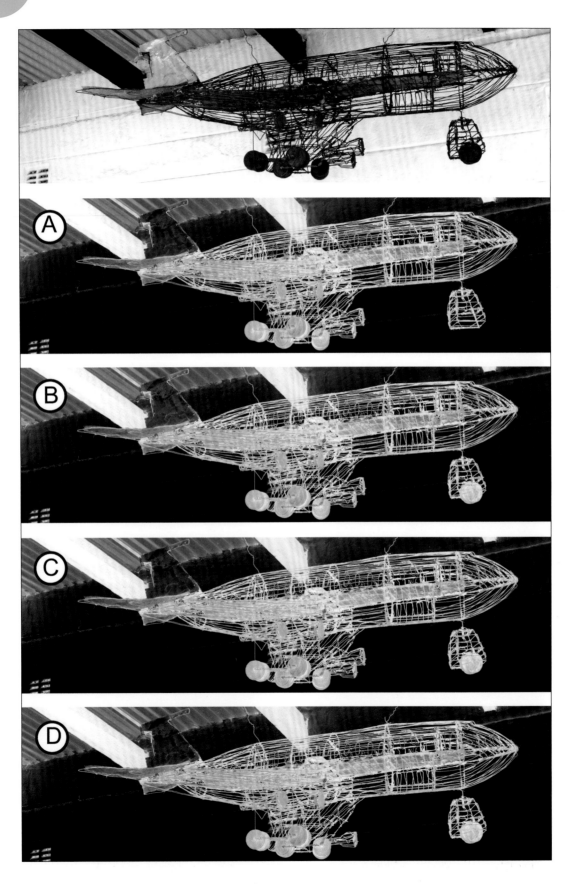

THE HORSE

1

2

3

4

5

THE HORSE

☐ ☐ ☐ ☐ ☐ ☐ ☐ ☐ ☐ ☐ ☐ ☐
1 2 3 4 5 6 7 8 9 10 11 12

1

2

3

4

5

JIGSAW PUZZLE

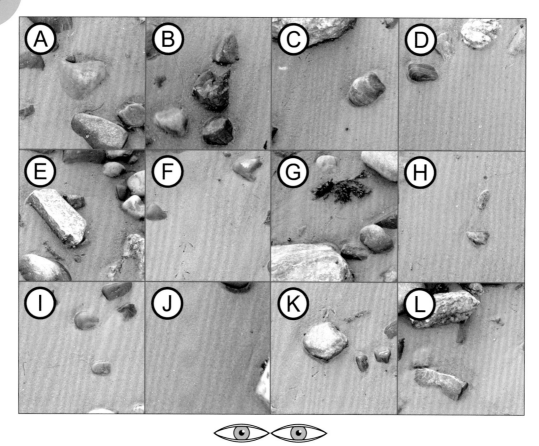

In which order should the twelve pictures above be placed,
in order to create an exact copy of the picture below?

HIDDEN CREATURES

The four creatures below have all been hidden in the black and white picture above. Can you spot them hiding in the trees?

15

1

2

3

4

5

1	2	3	4	5	6	7	8	9	10

16

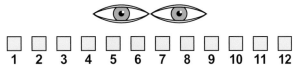

| 1 | 2 | 3 | 4 | 5 | 6 | 7 | 8 | 9 | 10 | 11 | 12 |

1

2

3

4

5

BOOKS

1

2

3

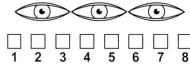

1	2	3	4	5	6	7	8

4

5

IN THE GARDEN

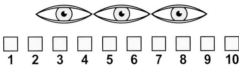

1	2	3	4	5	6	7	8	9	10

1

2

3

4

5

1

2

3

4

5

WALLHANGING

BOYS HANGING OUT

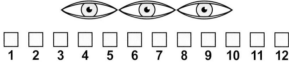

1	2	3	4	5	6	7	8	9	10	11	12

1

2

3

4

5

TRAINING SHOES

 1

 2

 3

4

 5

TRAINING SHOES

□ □ □ □ □ □ □ □ □ □
1 2 3 4 5 6 7 8 9 10

 1

 2

 3

 4

 5

1

2

3

4

5

CUTTING OUT

Of the six clips below, which is the only one to appear in the picture opposite?

VALVES

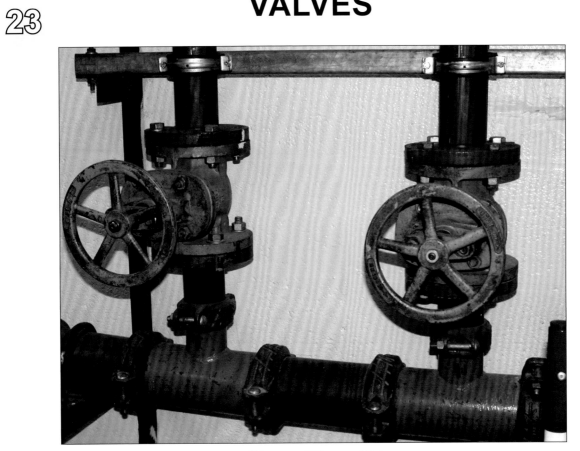

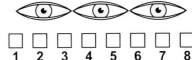

1 2 3 4 5 6 7 8

1

2

3

4

5

BEACH HUTS

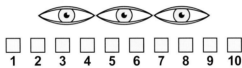

1	2	3	4	5	6	7	8	9	10
□	□	□	□	□	□	□	□	□	□

1

2

3

4

5

TURKEY

TURKEY

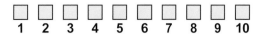

1

2

3

4

5

SWEETS IN REFLECTION

1

2

3

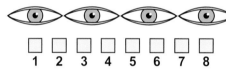

1 2 3 4 5 6 7 8

4

5

DRESS DISPLAY

27

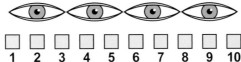

1	2	3	4	5	6	7	8	9	10

JIGSAW PUZZLE

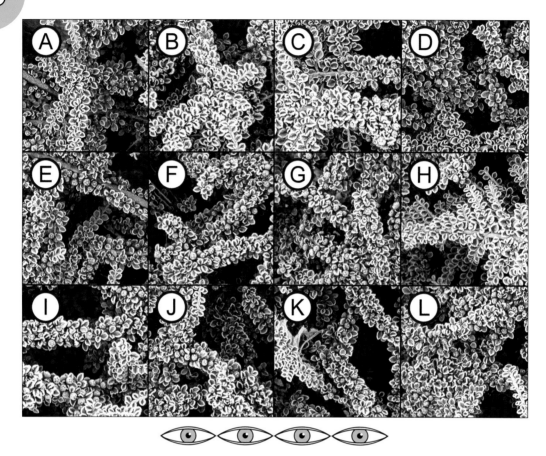

In which order should the twelve pictures above be placed,
in order to create an exact copy of the picture below?

CHINESE LANTERNS

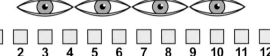

| 1 | 2 | 3 | 4 | 5 | 6 | 7 | 8 | 9 | 10 | 11 | 12 |

1

2

3

4

5

PAINTED LADY

PAINTED LADY

☐ ☐ ☐ ☐ ☐ ☐ ☐ ☐ ☐ ☐ ☐ ☐ ☐ ☐
1 2 3 4 5 6 7 8 9 10 11 12 13 14

1

2

3

4

5

TONGA LOINCLOTH

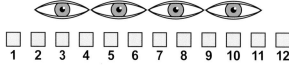

WATERFRONT

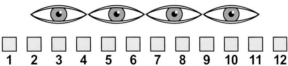

| 1 | 2 | 3 | 4 | 5 | 6 | 7 | 8 | 9 | 10 | 11 | 12 |

1

2

3

4

5

CLOCK

1

2

3

4

5

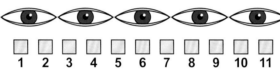

| 1 | 2 | 3 | 4 | 5 | 6 | 7 | 8 | 9 | 10 | 11 |

EXCAVATORS

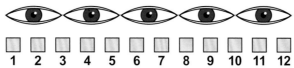

| 1 | 2 | 3 | 4 | 5 | 6 | 7 | 8 | 9 | 10 | 11 | 12 |

1

2

3

4

5

1

2

3

4

5

IN THE SUPERMARKET

SUCCULENTS

1

2

3

4

5

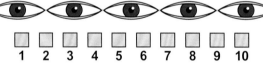

| 1 | 2 | 3 | 4 | 5 | 6 | 7 | 8 | 9 | 10 |

THE POND

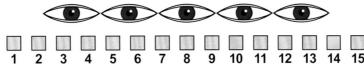

| | | | | | | | | | | | | | | |
|1|2|3|4|5|6|7|8|9|10|11|12|13|14|15|

1

2

3

4

5

38 CLOTH STALL IN REFLECTION

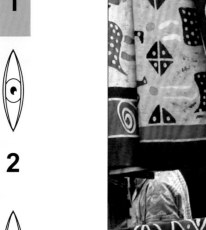

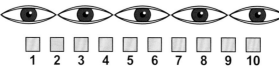

1 2 3 4 5 6 7 8 9 10

CHICKENS

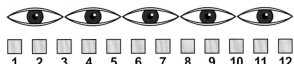

1 2 3 4 5 6 7 8 9 10 11 12

1

2

3

4

5

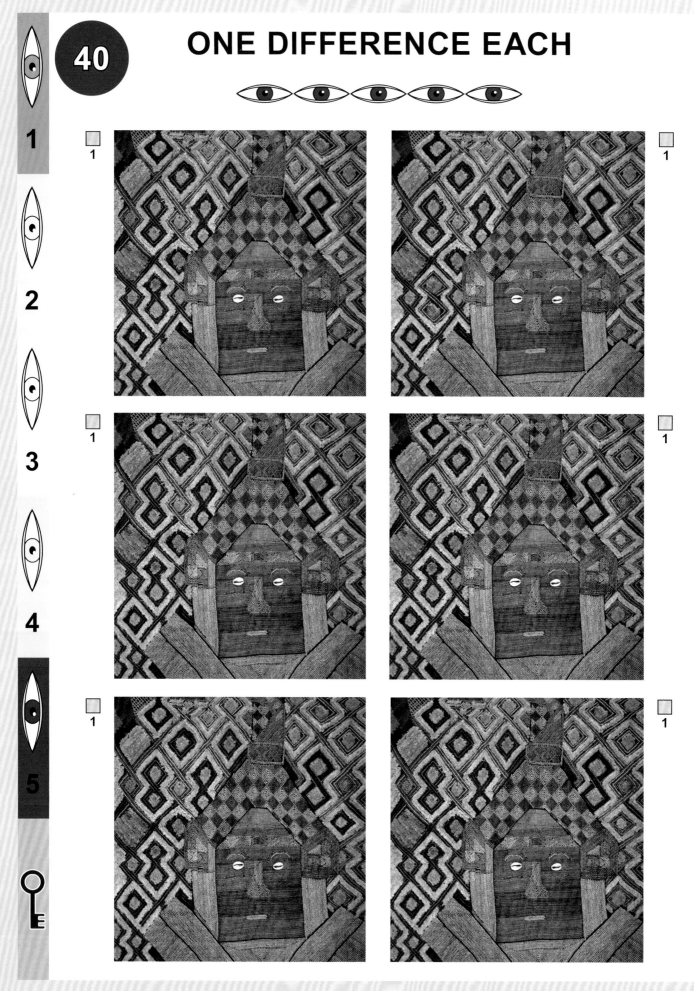

SOLUTIONS

1

2

3

4

5

6

7

8

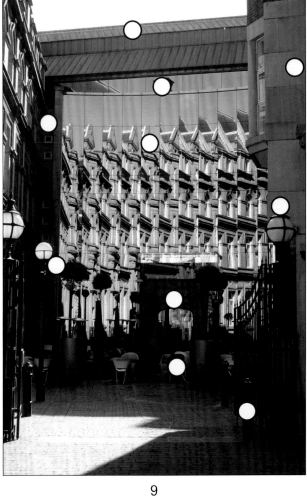

9

10

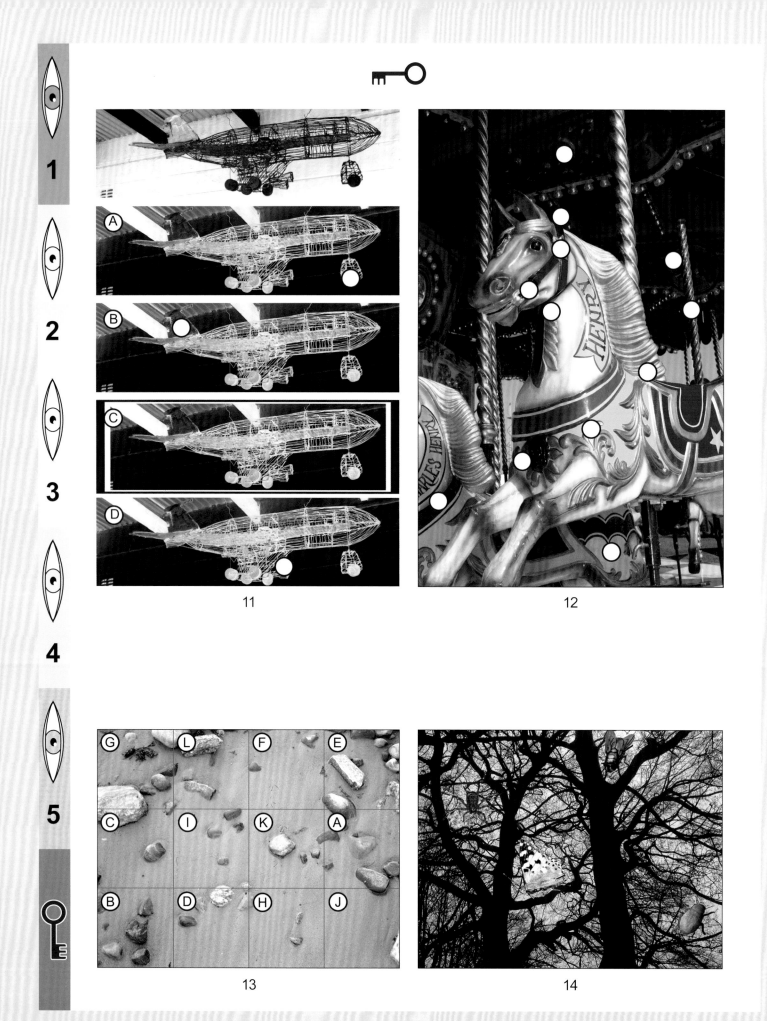

11

12

13

14

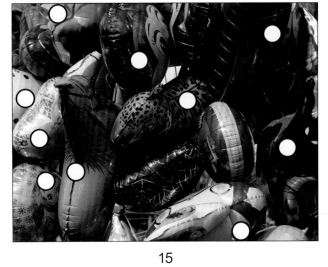

15

16

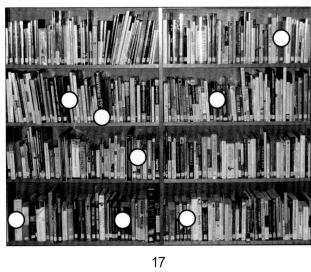

17

18

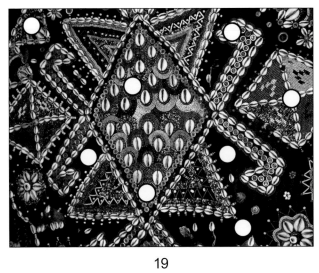

19

20

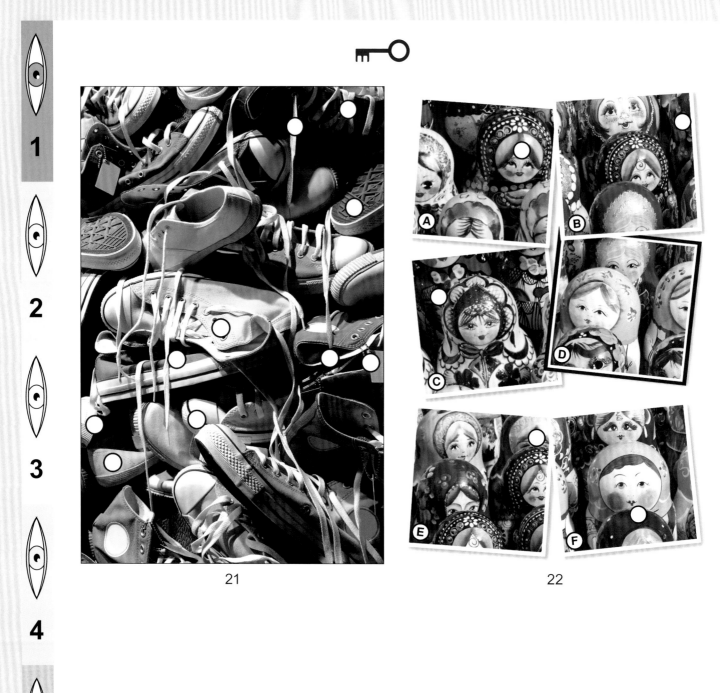

21

22

23

24

25

26

27

28

29

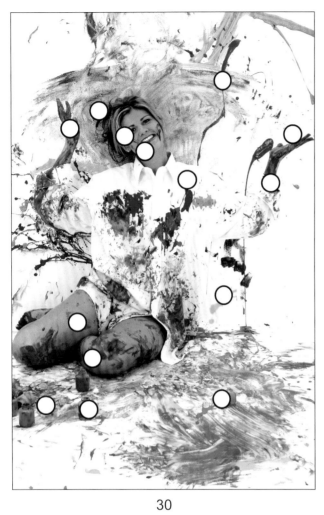

30

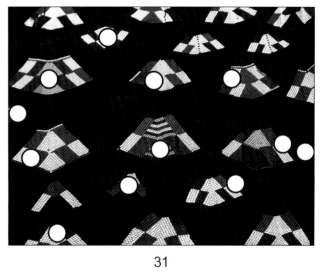

31

32

33

34

35

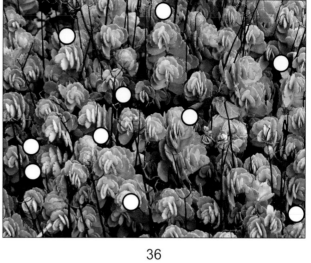

36

37

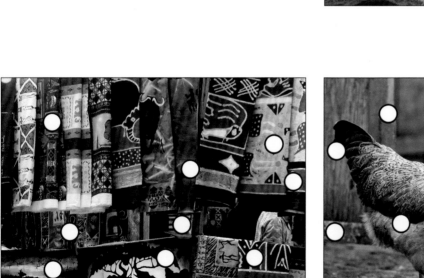

38

39

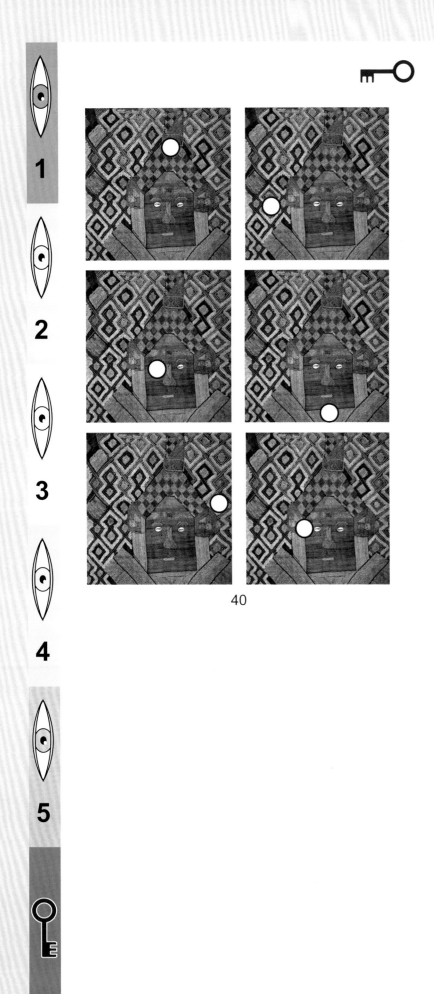

40